My Home and School

Table of Contents

ISBN: 9-780837-480435

Which House?

Good News! Sue is moving to Red Road. Read the rhymes. Write the house numbers on the signs. Find the house where Sue will live.

The house made of bricks is number six. **6**

A baby named Kevin lives in number seven. **7**

A cat up a tree is at number three. **3**

The house still not done is number one. **1**

A dog by a door is at number four. **4**

Bees in a hive are behind number five. **5**

A new home for Sue is number two. **2**

—Lana Kleinschmidt

What street do you live on?

On Your Own _____

Whose Room?

Ken is Sue's brother. He took a picture of his new bedroom.

—John Marinelli

Ken's Map

Then Ken made a map. It looks like the picture.

Left

Right

—Scott Bricher

1 Put a **B** on the bed in the picture.
Put a **B** on the bed on the map.

2 Put an **S** on the ship in the picture.
Put an **S** on the ship on the map.

On Your Own

3 Put a **D** on the desk in the picture.
Put a **D** on the desk on the map.

Use empty boxes to make a model of Ken's bedroom. Then make a model of your bedroom.

—AP/Wide World Photos

SAFE FROM A FIRE

A house caught on fire. The people knew how to get out quickly. They met at a tree. Firefighters put out the fire. All the people were safe.

Left and **right** are direction words. Look at the picture map. Read each sentence below. Write the direction words that tell where things are. The first has been done for you.

1 Go in the front door. A 🔥 is on the _____right_____.

2 The 🛏 is on the _____.

3 The 🪑 is on the _____.

4 The 🐱 is on the _____.

5 Circle the place near the where everyone met.

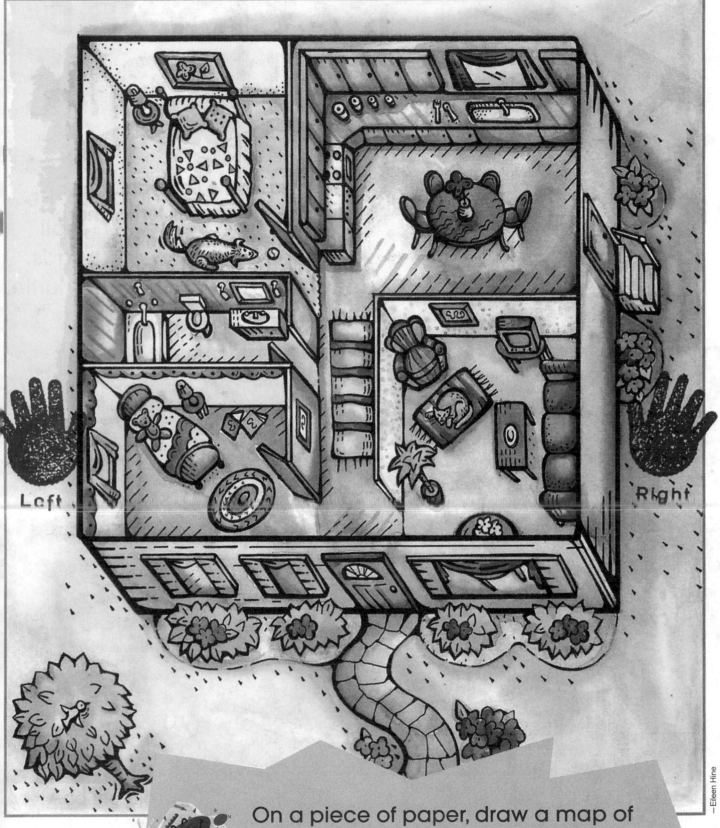

Left

Right

— Eileen Hine

On Your Own

On a piece of paper, draw a map of your home. Show two ways to get out. Set up a meeting place. Have a practice fire drill.

BACKYARD SURPRISE

Tony was in the backyard. He heard a noise. He saw a small turtle. The turtle had two heads. Tony took good care of the turtle. He named it Jon and Bob.

This is a picture of Tony's backyard.

1 Put an **x** on the tree near the picnic table.

2 Draw a fish in the pond.

3 Circle the sandbox.

Map Symbols, Place, Human/Environment Interactions

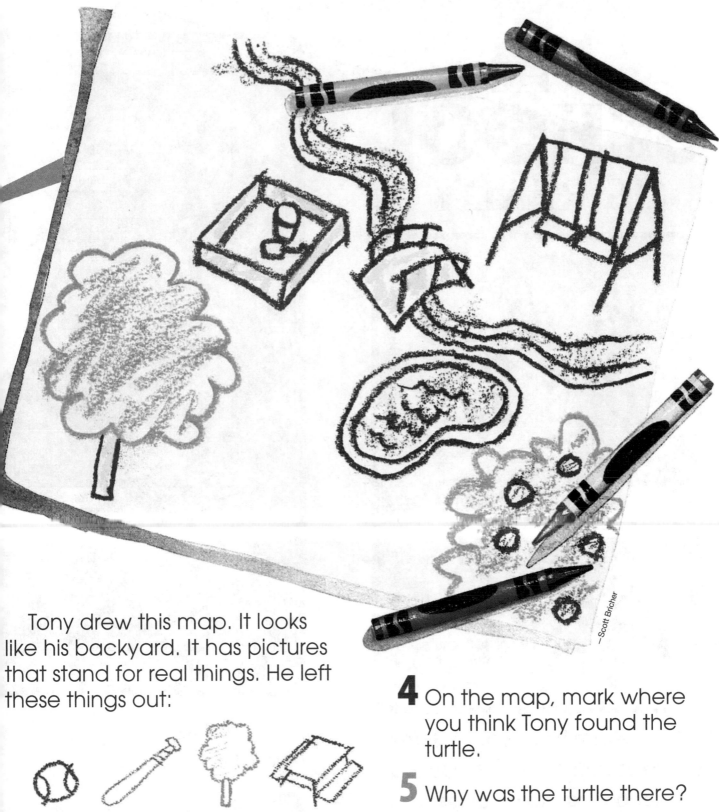

—Scott Bricher

Tony drew this map. It looks like his backyard. It has pictures that stand for real things. He left these things out:

1 Add the picnic table to the map.

2 Add the bat and ball to the map.

3 Add the other tree.

4 On the map, mark where you think Tony found the turtle.

5 Why was the turtle there?

_____

_____

_____

_____

THE SCHOOL IS READY

— Tom Salyer/Silver Image

— Debra Page-Trim

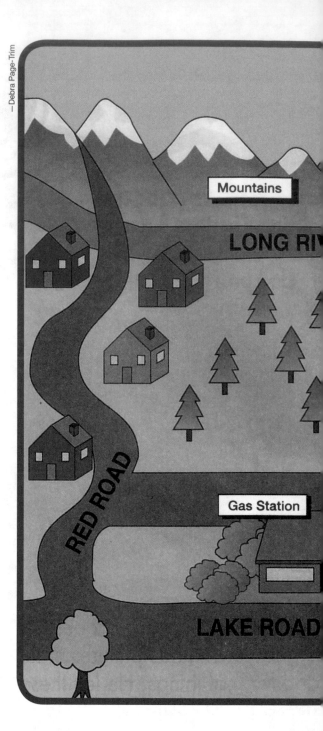

A big storm hit a school. Some windows broke. The roof leaked. The school had to be closed.

Workers put in new windows. They fixed the roof. Now children can go back to school.

Look at the map.
Follow the directions.

1 Ted and Rita live in the red house on Red Road. Show how they might go to school. Draw a line from their house to the school.

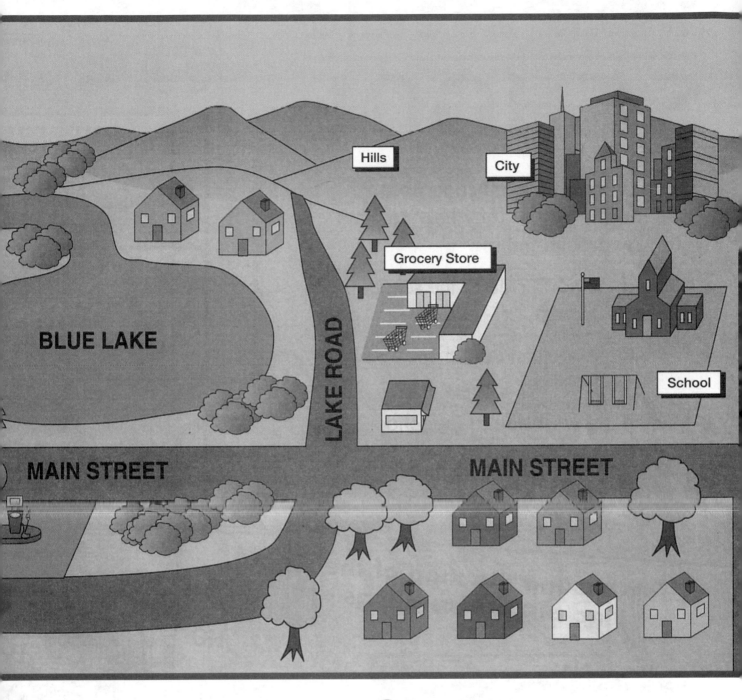

2 Draw a path from the yellow house near Main Street to the school.

3 Circle the green house near Blue Lake.

4 Draw a car in the GAS.

5 Put these things on the map.
- a 🚣 on the lake
- two ⛺ ⛺ near the lake

6 Draw two more things on your map.

Walk Around
SCHOOL

North, south, east, and **west** are direction words. They help you find your way around the school.

1 Find the north side of the school. Circle **North.**

2 Find the south side of the school. Circle **South.**

3 Find the west side of the school. Put a box around **West.**

4 Find the east side of the school. Put a box around **East.**

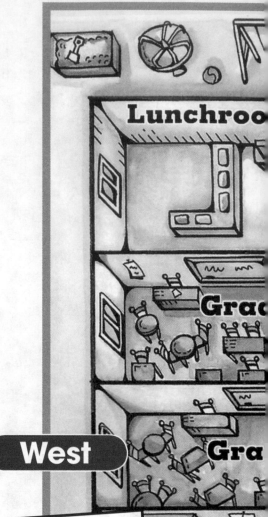

West

Look around the map of the school. Find out where things are.

Check **Yes** or **No.**

	YES	NO
❶ The lunchroom is on the **north** side.		
❷ Three classrooms are on the **west** side.		
❸ The principal's office is on the **east** side.		
❹ The bathrooms are on the **south** side.		
❺ The nurse's office is on the **west** side.		

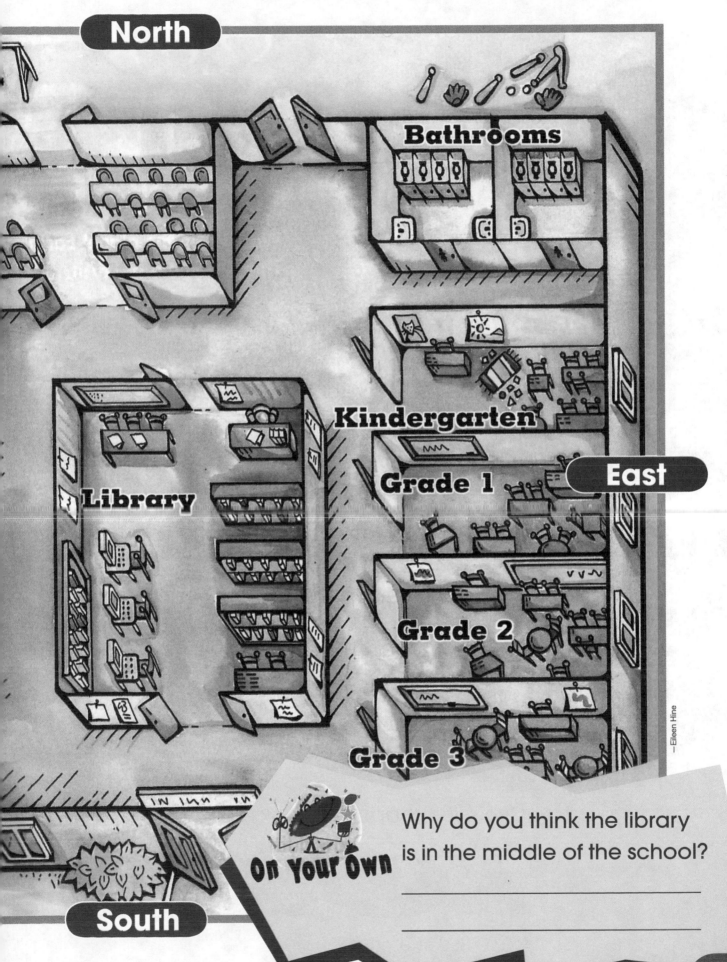

North

Bathrooms

Kindergarten

Grade 1

East

Library

Grade 2

Grade 3

—Eileen Hine

On Your Own

Why do you think the library is in the middle of the school?

_____

_____

South

Our GLOBE

We live on the planet Earth. This is a photo of Earth.

Circle the shape that looks like Earth.

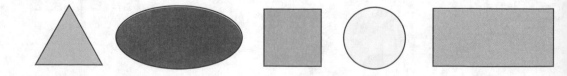

North

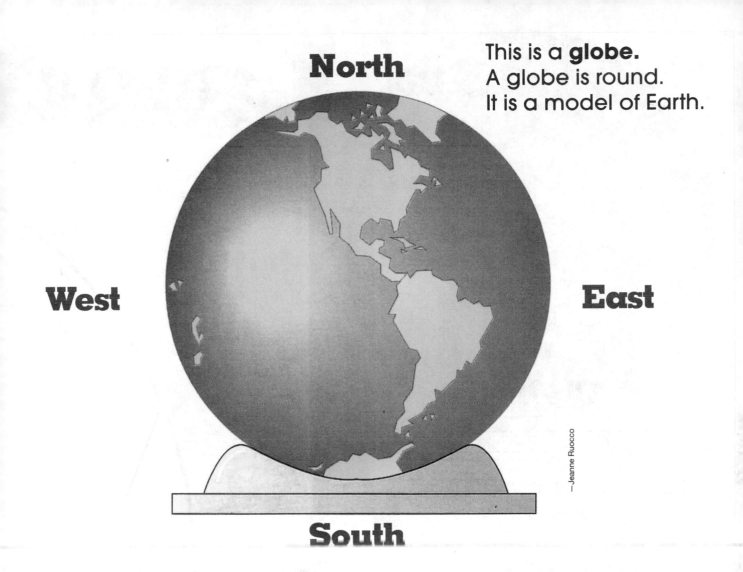

This is a **globe.**
A globe is round.
It is a model of Earth.

West

East

South

— Jeanne Ruocco

North is toward the North Pole.
South is toward the South Pole.
West is to the left.
East is to the right.

Draw a line from **North** to
South on the globe above.

Draw a line from **West** to **East.**

You have made a drawing
of a **compass rose.**

A compass rose shows **N**orth, **S**outh,
East, and **W**est. Sometimes, only the
first letter of each word is used.

Finish this compass rose:

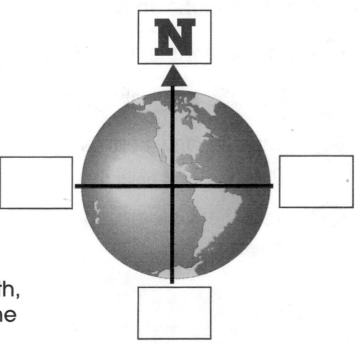

N

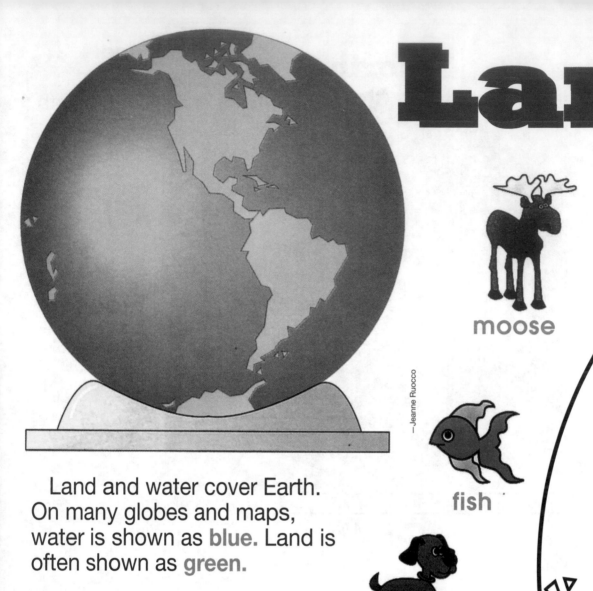

Land

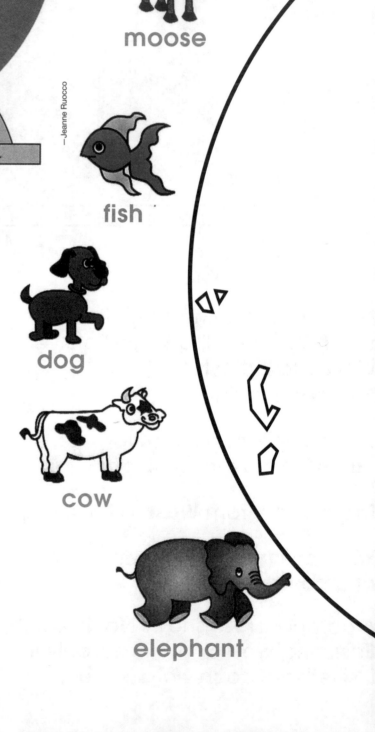

—Jeanne Ruocco

moose

fish

dog

cow

elephant

Land and water cover Earth. On many globes and maps, water is shown as **blue.** Land is often shown as **green.**

Make the big globe on the right look like the globe above.

1 Color the water light **blue.**

2 Color the land light **green.**

3 Draw the land animals on land.

4 Draw the water animals on water.

and Water

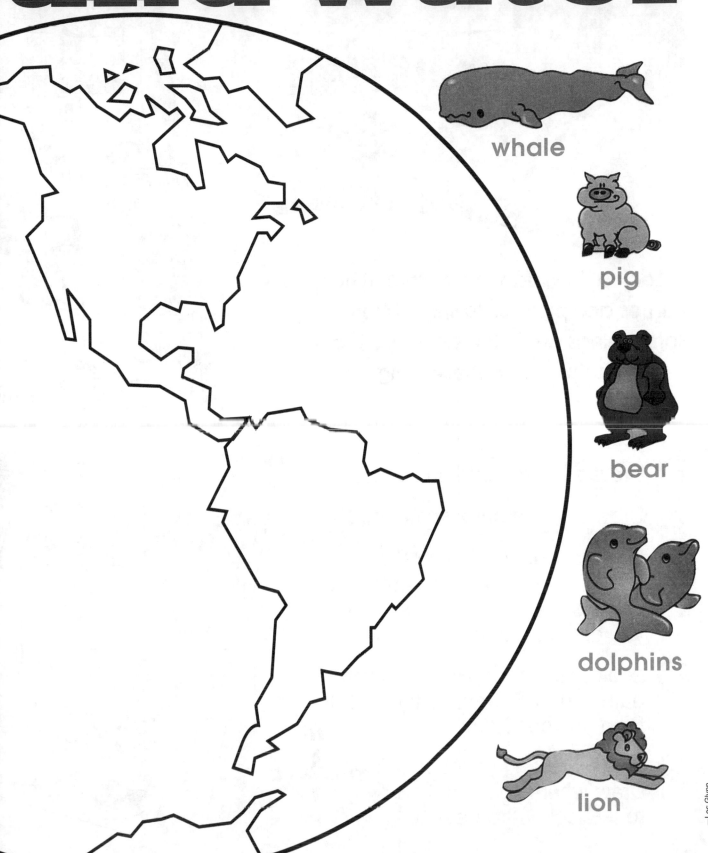

whale

pig

bear

dolphins

lion

—Lee Glynn

New Supermarket Opens

Look at this map of the store. It has names and pictures to show where some things are in the store. Use the map to help you do these things.

1 Draw a ◯ around some candy.

2 Draw a ▢ around some meat.

3 Draw a △ around some fruit.

4 Now use the map to go shopping. The entrance is on the south side of the supermarket. Put an **X** where you go into the store.

5 Look at the shopping list. Mark a path you might take to find the food on your list.

6 Finish marking your path. Draw where you might go to a checkout to pay.

Shopping list
Pie
Bananas
Milk
Cereal
Carrots
Meat

On Your Own

Find two more things you would like to buy. Circle them on the map.

Let's Go to the Mall

A mall has many stores. Look at this map of a mall. One entrance is on the **south.** Put an **X** on that entrance.

Start there. Draw a path through the mall to find the things on the list. Circle each thing as you find it in the mall.

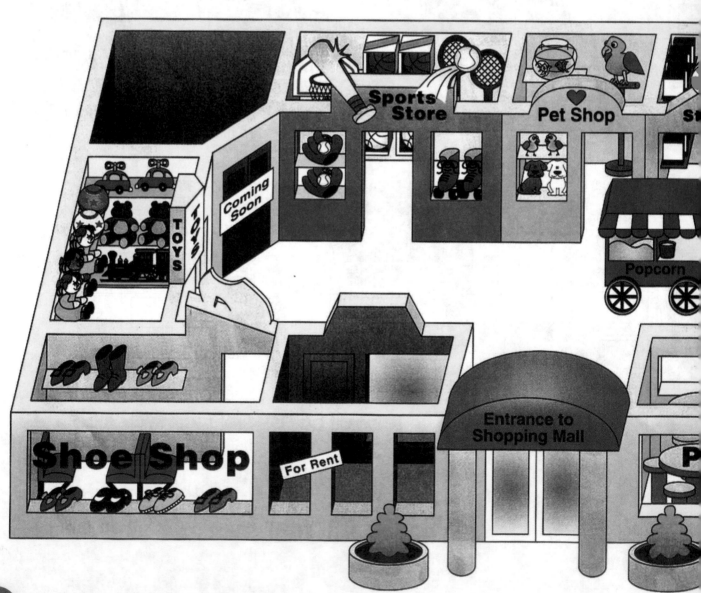

roller skates

parrot

shoes

wind-up car

pizza

Look at the map. Write the word **north, south, east,** or **west** to finish each sentence.

1 The sports store is on the

_____

side of the mall.

2 The pizza store is on the

_____

side of the mall.

3 The toy store is on the

_____

side of the mall.

4 The department store is on the

_____

side of the mall.

On Your Own Find two empty stores in the mall. What would you put in these empty stores? Why?

_____

_____

_____

—Lee Glynn

21

Zoo News

Follow the directions to see a new baby.

1 Start at the zoo entrance. Draw a path **north** to the dot by the tigers.

2 Follow the path **east** to the next dot by the elephants.

3 At the dot, go **north** to the next dot.

4 Go **west** past the seals to the next dot.

5 Turn **south.** Stop at the next dot. Circle the new baby animal.

Choose and write the name of a zoo animal...

(**monkeys   seals   zebras   tigers**)

in the **north** _____ ,

in the **south** _____ ,

in the **east** _____ ,

and in the **west** _____ .

**It's opening day at the Summer Park.
The park has four parts. The signs will
help you find your way around.**

1 On the map, underline the names of the four parts of the park.

2 Circle the water slide on the map. Which part of the park is it in?

_____

3 Find a place where you can buy ice cream. Which part of the park is it in?

_____

4 Mark a path from the Entrance to the Ferris wheel. Does your path go **north** or **south?**

_____

5 Put an **X** on the show. Which part of the park is it in?

_____

6 Mark a path from the Ferris wheel to the fountain. Does your path go **north** or **south?**

_____

7 Mark a path from the fountain to the boats. Does your path go **east** or **west?**

_____

8 Put a √ on the place you would go next. Mark the path you would follow to get there.

Region, Movement, Human/Environment Interactions

Summer Park

RIDES

WATER FUN

SHOWS

ICE CREAM

FOOD

ENTRANCE

—Blake Thornton

N
W E
S

On Your Own

Draw yourself next to what you like best in the park.

Mr. Bush Goes to Washington, D.C.

George W. Bush was the governor of Texas. He was elected president of the United States two times. He and his family live in Washington, D.C.

President Bush and Mrs. Bush with their daughters Jenna and Barbara.

1 Put an **X** on Texas.

2 Find the star that shows Washington, D.C. Circle that star.

3 Draw a line from Texas to Washington, D.C.

4 Circle the ways that Mr. Bush might travel to Washington, D.C.

5 Draw a line to show how he could travel by boat.

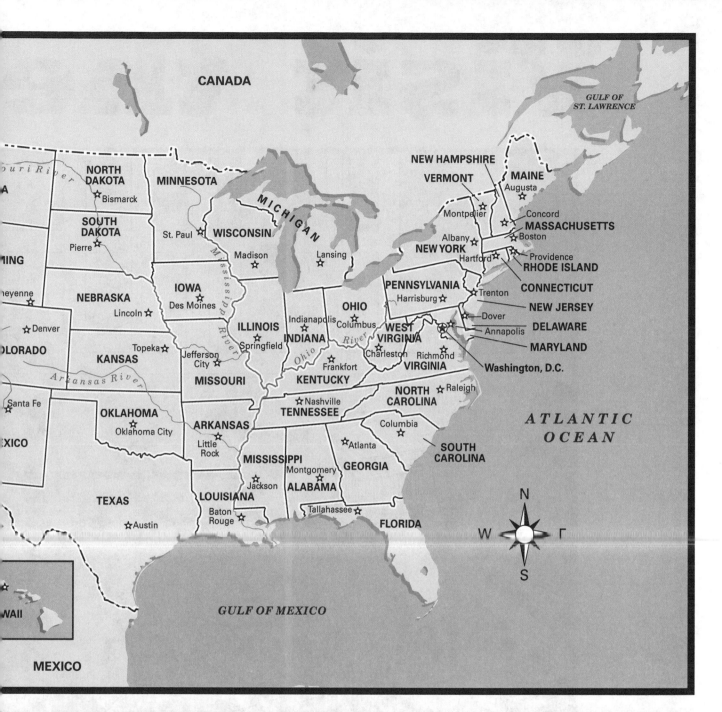

Read each sentence. √ the correct answer.	Yes	No
1 Washington, D.C., is **east** of Texas.		
2 President Bush went **south** to get to Washington, D.C.		
3 President Bush crossed a river on his trip.		
4 To go back to Texas, President Bush will go **west**.		

Visit the

—Debra Page-Tine

Map Key

White House

Jefferson
Memorial

Reflecting Poo

Capital

Washington Monument **Lincoln Memorial**

Washington, D.C., is the capital of the United States. There are many special places to visit.

Look at the map of Washington, D.C. It has a map key. The map key uses pictures and words to help you find your way.

1 Find the White House on the map. Mark a path from the White House to the Washington Monument. Did you go **north** or **south?**

_____

2 Mark a path from the Washington Monument to the Lincoln Memorial. Did you go **east** or **west?**

_____

3 Mark a path from the Lincoln Memorial to the Jefferson Memorial.

4 Mark a path from the Jefferson Memorial to the White House. Did you go **east** or **north?**

_____

Visit the

Make this map your own special Map.

1 Find the state you live in. Draw a picture of your face in or near your state.

2 Choose a state to visit. Draw a line under its name.

3 Mark a path from your state to the state you are going to visit. Underline the names of the states you will go through.

4 Think of the different ways people can travel. Which way do you think would be the most fun way to travel? Why?

_____

_____

_____

_____

_____

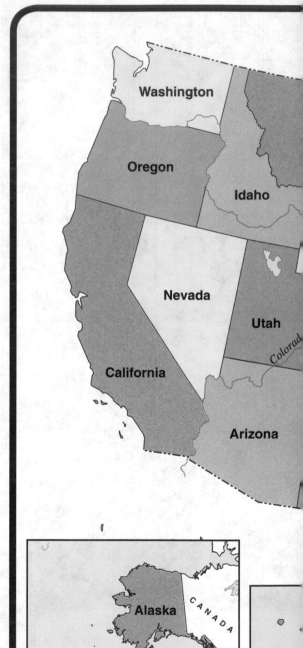

—Larry Tortice

U.S.A.

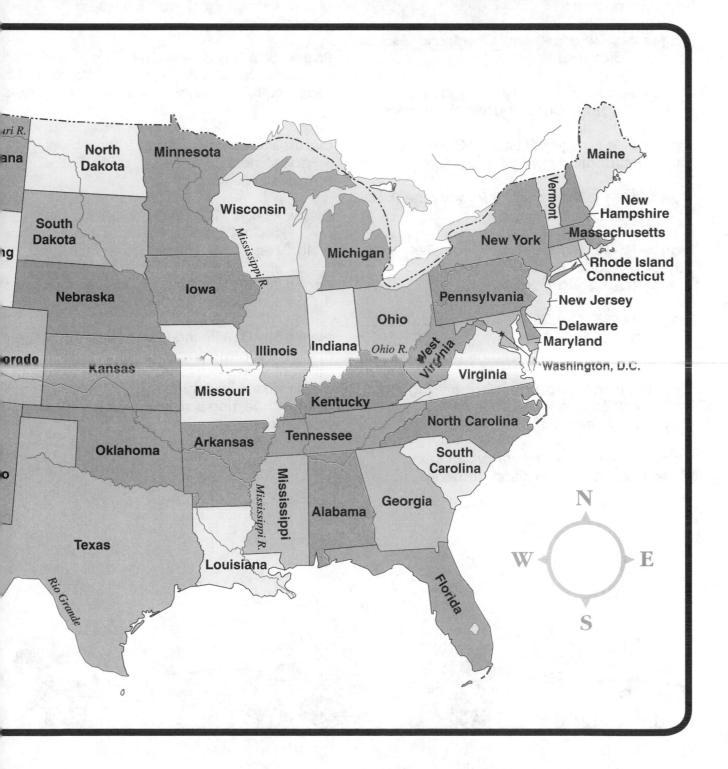

North Dakota

Minnesota

Maine

Wisconsin

Vermont

New Hampshire

South Dakota

Michigan

New York

Massachusetts

Nebraska

Iowa

Mississippi R.

Rhode Island
Connecticut

Pennsylvania

New Jersey

Ohio

Delaware
Maryland

orado

Kansas

Illinois

Indiana

Ohio R.

West Virginia

Virginia

Washington, D.C.

Missouri

Kentucky

North Carolina

Oklahoma

Arkansas

Tennessee

South Carolina

Mississippi R.

Mississippi

Alabama

Georgia

Texas

Rio Grande

Louisiana

Florida

N

W   E

S

Answer Key

Pages 2-3: *Which House?* Check and discuss students' answers.

Pages 4-5: *Whose Room?* Check and discuss students' drawings.

Pages 6-7: *Safe from a Fire:* 1. right. 2. left. 3. right. 4. right. 5. Check students' drawings.

Pages 8-9: *Backyard Surprise:* Check and discuss students' drawings and answers.

Pages 10-11: *The School Is Ready:* Check and discuss students' drawings.

Pages 12-13: *Walk Around School:* 1-4. Check and discuss students' drawings. 1. Yes. 2. Yes. 3. No. 4. No. 5. Yes.

Pages 14-15: *Our Globe:* Check and discuss students' drawings.

Pages 16-17: *Land and Water:* Land animals are the moose, dog, cow, elephant, pig, bear, and lion. Water animals are the fish, whale, and dolphins.

Pages 18-19: *New Supermarket Opens:* Check and discuss students' drawings.

Pages 20-21: *Let's Go to the Mall:* Check students' drawings. 1. north. 2. south. 3. west. 4. east.

Pages 22-23: *Zoo News:* 1-5. Check and discuss students' drawings. Zoo Animals: north seals, south/monkeys, east/zebras, west/tigers.

Pages 24-25: *Opening Day:* 1. Check and discuss students' responses. 2. Water Fun. 3. Food. 4. north. 5. Shows. 6. south. 7. east. 8. Answers will vary.

Pages 26-27: *Mr. Bush Goes to Washington, D.C.:* 1-5. Check students' responses. 1. Yes. 2. No. 3. Yes. 4. Yes. (He will go south too.)

Pages 28-29: *Visit the Capital:* 1. south. 2. west. 3. Check students' drawings. 4. north.

Pages 30-31: *Visit the U.S.A.:* Check and discuss students' maps and answers. Discuss different ways people travel and help your class make a list, including car, truck, trailer, boat, canoe, horse, train, bicycle, skates, and plane.